Agree
Or
Disagree

52 WRITING PROMPTS FOR OPINION ESSAYS

For permission requests, write to the publisher "ATTN: Permissions", at the address below:

Alphabet Publishing

1204 Main Street #172

Branford, CT 06405 USA

info@alphabetpublishingbooks.com

www.alphabetpublishingbooks.com

Discounts on class sets and bulk orders available upon inquiry.

Why Write Argument Essays?

Argument essays are common on standardized tests such as the TOEFL, TOEIC, and IATEFL, and even university admissions exams or applications. Being able to write persuasively is a test not only of your vocabulary and grammar, but also your ability to construct an argument, distinguish between fact, evaluate evidence, and organize an essay.

For this reason, these prompts make good critical thinking practice. They can be used to write a short paragraph, rather than a full essay or even just an outline.

Academic debates also take the form of a statement with one team agreeing and another disagreeing. In formal debates, students typically cannot choose sides. It's good practice (and fun) to write an essay arguing one side of the issue and then another arguing the opposite.

Persuasive writing is also a genre that is found outside the classroom and the ivy tower. Business memos proposing or discouraging action, fund-raising letters, marketing emails, print advertisements, letters to the editor, political position papers, loan applications, contest entries, cover letters for a job: all of these require persuasive writing to some extent.

Kinds of Evidence

One of the most important features of a persuasive essay is the evidence you use. You may be a very beautiful writer, but the facts and the evidence must be on your side. There are many kinds of evidence, but here are some examples of the most common kind employed.

Note: Be sure to know what kinds of references your teacher requires. You don't want to accidentally plagiarize.

Thesis: Getting exercise can improve your mood.

Explanation:
Exercise promotes a variety of changes in the brain that make you feel good.

Cause-and-effect reasoning:
Exercise causes your body to release a hormone called endorphins. Endorphins react with your brain. They cause your brain to reduce its perception of pain. In fact, endorphins cause a general feeling of well-being. This feeling combined with a lack of pain puts you in a better mood.

Facts:
30 minutes of strenuous exercise, in which your heart rate is at 90-160 beats per minute, is enough to release endorphins into your system. A recent study by the Harvard School of Medicine concluded that running is the most efficient exercise for releasing endorphins.

Comparison:
People who exercise every day are in better health than people who do not and poor health is a major cause of unhappiness.

Citing an authority:
Dr. Vivek Murthy, Surgeon General of the United States, published a paper on Exercise (Murphy 2016) in which he said, "Regular exercise leads to better sleep, better memory, and less stress."

Outlining a Persuasive Essay

There are a few ways to organize an argument essay. If you are writing a letter or a memo for work, your structure may be more flexible. However, if you are writing an essay for a standardized test or the classroom, the standards tend to be stricter.

Two common ways to structure an essay include the argument-evidence model and the opposing-argument-rebuttal mode.

ARGUMENT-EVIDENCE MODEL

I.   Introduction
   A. Hook
   B. Context
   C. Thesis
II. Body paragraph
   A. Statement of first argument
   B. Evidence supporting first argument
   C. Summary tying back to thesis
III. Body paragraph
   A. Statement of second argument
   B. Evidence supporting second argument
   C. Summary tying back to thesis
IV. Body paragraph
   A. Statement of second argument
   B. Evidence supporting second argument
   C. Summary tying back to thesis
V.   Conclusion
   A. Summary of the evidence
   B. Repetition of the thesis
   C. Caveats and qualifications

OPPOSING ARGUMENT-REBUTTAL MODEL

This model, which may seem counter-intuitive at first, asks you to start your body paragraphs with an opposing argument. An opposing argument is something that a person disagreeing with you might say. You then show why the opposing argument is wrong.

This model can be difficult to master, but it can also be quite convincing. It shows that you understand the reasons someone may disagree with you. Then, it gives you a chance to disarm those reasons, meaning you are speaking directly to people who may not agree with you!

    I.   Introduction

        A. Hook

        B. Context

        C. Thesis

   II. Body paragraph

        A. Statement of first opposing argument]

        B. Rebuttal of opposing argument

        C. Evidence supporting rebuttal

        D. Summary tying back to thesis

  III. Body paragraph

        A. Statement of second opposing argument

        B. Rebuttal of opposing argument

        C. Evidence supporting rebuttal

        D. Summary tying back to thesis

Body paragraph

        A. Statement of any arguments not already addressed

        B. Evidence supporting those arguments

        C. Summary tying back to thesis

  IV. Conclusion

        A. Summary of the evidence

        B. Repetition of the thesis

        C. Caveats and qualifications

Useful Language for Persuasive Essays

To express an opinion

I think that ...

I believe

It seems clear [to me] that

For these reasons …

Because of this, I believe that …

The evidence shows …

In short, …

I argue …

To hedge

It is likely that …

It seems clear that …

The most likely answer is that ….

The facts seem to show …

To give evidence and details

For example,

In fact,

For instance,

As X wrote, "...

What is more,

Furthermore,

One reason,

In addition

To introduce opposing arguments

Some people say …

Some may argue that …

Many people believe that … but this is not true.

To rebut

Despite what people think,

In fact, the case is …

However, ….

On the other hand, ….

The facts say ….

I do not agree ….

To summarize

In conclusion,

For this reason,

We must conclude that …

Therefore,

The evidence suggests

Clearly,

Name: _____   Date: _____

AGREE OR DISAGREE

The most important reason to go to university is to gain
knowledge so you can get a better job.

↔

Name: _____   Date: _____

AGREE OR DISAGREE
Parents are the best teachers.

↔

_____

_____

_____

_____

_____

_____

_____

_____

_____

_____

_____

_____

_____

_____

_____

_____

_____

_____

_____

_____

_____

_____

_____

AGREE OR DISAGREE

Being able to eat in restaurants or buy premade food has made
modern life better.

↔

AGREE OR DISAGREE

You learn more from experience than you do in books.

$\leftrightarrow$

_____
_____
_____
_____
_____
_____
_____
_____
_____
_____
_____
_____
_____
_____
_____
_____
_____
_____
_____
_____
_____
_____
_____
_____

AGREE OR DISAGREE

The most important thing a local government can do is bring
more businesses to town.

↔

AGREE OR DISAGREE

Violent movies, television shows, and video games make
people violent.

↔

AGREE OR DISAGREE

Smartphones are nothing more than distractions from real life.

↔

Name: _____   Date: _____

AGREE OR DISAGREE
Thanks to computers and technology, learning social skills is no longer important.

↔

_____

_____

_____

_____

_____

_____

_____

_____

_____

_____

_____

_____

_____

_____

_____

_____

_____

_____

_____

_____

_____

_____

_____

AGREE OR DISAGREE

Sports arenas are a waste of money. We should have more
educational facilities like museums instead.

↔

_____

_____

_____

_____

_____

_____

_____

_____

_____

_____

_____

_____

_____

_____

_____

_____

_____

_____

_____

_____

_____

_____

AGREE OR DISAGREE

It is better to raise children in a big city than a rural village.

↔

AGREE OR DISAGREE

When people succeed, it is because of hard work. Luck has
nothing to do with success

↔

AGREE OR DISAGREE

Universities in the US should give the same amount of money to academics as they do to sports.

↔

AGREE OR DISAGREE
Zoos should be outlawed because it is wrong to lock wild animals up.

↔

_____
_____
_____
_____
_____
_____
_____
_____
_____
_____
_____
_____
_____
_____
_____
_____
_____
_____
_____
_____
_____
_____

Name: _____   Date: _____

AGREE OR DISAGREE

Travelling to new places is a waste of time and money.

↔

AGREE OR DISAGREE

The so-called great artists and authors are not necessarily very good.
We only study them because everyone decided they are great.

↔

AGREE OR DISAGREE

It is better for a child to grow up with two parents, even
unhappy parents, than to go through a divorce.

↔

AGREE OR DISAGREE
University students should not be required to attend classes.
They are old enough to manage their own learning.
↔

Name: _____ Date: _____

AGREE OR DISAGREE

Friends are more important than family because you choose
your friends.

←→

Name: _____   Date: _____

AGREE OR DISAGREE
It is easier to learn by yourself than with a teacher.

↔

AGREE OR DISAGREE

Entertainers such as singers, actors, and athletes make
too much money.

←→

AGREE OR DISAGREE
In a democracy, people should be required to vote by law.

↔

_____

_____

_____

_____

_____

_____

_____

_____

_____

_____

_____

_____

_____

_____

_____

_____

_____

_____

_____

_____

_____

_____

_____

_____

Name: _____   Date: _____

AGREE OR DISAGREE
Everyone should go to university.

↔

AGREE OR DISAGREE
A good boss needs to be strict with their workers.

↔

_____

_____

_____

_____

_____

_____

_____

_____

_____

_____

_____

_____

_____

_____

_____

_____

_____

_____

_____

_____

_____

_____

_____

_____

_____

AGREE OR DISAGREE
The government should spend more money on public
transportation than fixing roads
↔

AGREE OR DISAGREE

Governments should not send aid to other countries. They
should take care of their own citizens first.

↔

AGREE OR DISAGREE

It is good to live in the same town or city for your whole life.

↔

AGREE OR DISAGREE

Communicating with people from other countries or cultures
makes us into better people.

↔

Name: _____ Date: _____

AGREE OR DISAGREE

It's better to save your money for the future than spend it
immediately.

↔

AGREE OR DISAGREE

Businesses should hire employees for their entire lives.

↔

AGREE OR DISAGREE

Attending a live performance of a play or concert or sports
match is more fun than watching it on TV.

↔

Name: _____   Date: _____

AGREE OR DISAGREE
Change is always good.

$$\leftrightarrow$$

Name: _____   Date: _____

AGREE OR DISAGREE

Learning about the past is not important because we live in the present.

↔

_____

_____

_____

_____

_____

_____

_____

_____

_____

_____

_____

_____

_____

_____

_____

_____

_____

_____

_____

_____

_____

AGREE OR DISAGREE

Democracy is ineffective because usually the people who vote
don't know enough to make good choices.

↔

Name: _____   Date: _____

AGREE OR DISAGREE
The government should pay people a regular salary.

↔

AGREE OR DISAGREE

With the help of technology, students are learning more and learning it better than before.

↔

Name: _____   Date: _____

AGREE OR DISAGREE
Never, never give up on your dreams, no matter what.

↔

_____

_____

_____

_____

_____

_____

_____

_____

_____

_____

_____

_____

_____

_____

_____

_____

_____

_____

_____

_____

AGREE OR DISAGREE

The government should make college or university free for
everyone.

↔

Name: _____   Date: _____

AGREE OR DISAGREE

Human needs are more important than animal or plant needs, so people should be able to build or use as much land as they want.

⇆

AGREE OR DISAGREE

Schools should teach basic skills like balancing a bank account, changing a tire on a car, making a household budget, and cooking.

↔

AGREE OR DISAGREE

Only crazy people are attracted to dangerous sports or
dangerous activities like skydiving or bungee jumping.

↔

AGREE OR DISAGREE

Taking taxes to pay for public services is wrong. People should be able to keep their money and pay for public services themselves.

⇇⇉

Name: _____   Date: _____

AGREE OR DISAGREE
It's better to wake up early than to stay up late.

↔

_____

_____

_____

_____

_____

_____

_____

_____

_____

_____

_____

_____

_____

_____

_____

_____

_____

_____

_____

_____

_____

_____

AGREE OR DISAGREE
A child should always be loyal to their parents, no matter what.

↔

_____

_____

_____

_____

_____

_____

_____

_____

_____

_____

_____

_____

_____

_____

_____

_____

_____

_____

_____

_____

_____

_____

_____

_____

AGREE OR DISAGREE
A parent should always be loyal to their children, no
matter what.
↔

AGREE OR DISAGREE

It is better to work for a small company than a large corporation.

↔

Name: _____   Date: _____

AGREE OR DISAGREE

People only work because they need money to live.

↔

AGREE OR DISAGREE

Talking to someone face-to-face is better than communicating
through letters, email, or messaging.

↔

AGREE OR DISAGREE

It's better to get good at one thing than learn to do lots of different things.

←→

AGREE OR DISAGREE

Success in life comes from taking risks, not careful planning.

←→

AGREE OR DISAGREE

You should never judge a person by their external appearance.

↔

AGREE OR DISAGREE

Someday computers and robots will replace human beings in every job.

↔

AGREE OR DISAGREE
Healthcare should be free for everyone.

←→

_____
_____
_____
_____
_____
_____
_____
_____
_____
_____
_____
_____
_____
_____
_____
_____
_____
_____
_____
_____
_____

OTHER WRITING JOURNALS FROM ALPHABET PUBLISHING

Reflections Weekly Writing Journal:
52 Prompts about You

Inspirations Weekly Writing Journal:
52 Prompts for Short Stories

Comparisons: 52 Writing Prompts for
Compare/Contrast Essays

Case Studies: 52 Writing Prompts for
Problem/Solution Essays

Draw and Write: Writing Journal for
Young Learners

Picture Prompts Writing Journal

We are a small, independent publishing company that specializes in creative resources for teachers in the area of English Language Arts and English as a Second or Other Language. We help stock the teacher toolkit with practical, useful, and innovative materials.

Lightning Source UK Ltd.
Milton Keynes UK
UKHW031931031220
374578UK00008B/2008